MY LITTLE CABBAGE

J. B. LIPPINCOTT COMPANY / PHILADELPHIA / NEW YORK

MY LITTLE
"CABBAGE"

MON PETIT CHOU

by Susan Purdy

For Geoffrey

I live in the UNITED STATES

I am called Tommy,

but that is not all . . .

My grandma calls me

"My little monkey."

My mother calls me

"My little devil."

My father calls me

"My little lamb."

BUT THIS IS

THE
REAL
ME!

I live in FRANCE

I am called Annique,

but that is not all . . .

My mother calls me

"Mon petit chou"
(mohn p'tee shoo)

"My little cabbage."

LEGUMES

My papa calls me

"Mon petit lapin"
(mohn p'tee lah-pehn')

"My little rabbit."

My aunt calls me

"Ma petite cocotte"
(mah p'teet koh-koht')

"My little casserole."

BUT THIS IS THE REAL ME!

I live in SWEDEN

I am called Lars, but that is not all . . .

My mother calls me

"Min lilla groda"

(min li'-lah groo'-dah)

"My little frog."

My brother calls me

"Lilla gris"
(li'-lah grees)

"Little piggy."

My grandpa calls me

"Hjärte-gull"
(yer'-teh gul)

"Heart of gold."

BUT THIS IS

THE
REAL
ME!

I live in RUSSIA

I am called Sergei,

but that is not all . . .

My mother says

О, ТЫ МОЙ ЦВЕТОЧЕК
(oh tee moy tsve-to'-chek)

"My little flower."

My uncle calls me

УХ, ТЫ МАЛЕНЬКИЙ МЕДВЕЖОНОК
(ookh tee ma'-len-key med-vezh-o'-nok)

"My little bear."

My father calls me

МЕЛЕНЬКИЙ ГЕРОЙ
(ma'-len-key ge-roy')

"Little hero."

BUT THIS

IS

THE

REAL ME!

I live in GREECE

I am called Katiaki,

but that is not all . . .

My mother calls me

ΠΑΠΑΚΙ ΜΟΥ
(pa-pa'-kee moo)

"My little duck."

My father calls me

KOYKΛAKI MOY
(koo-klah'-ki moo)

"My little doll."

My grandma calls me

MΩPO MOY
(mo-roh' moo)

"My little baby."

BUT THIS IS

THE
REAL
ME!

I live in EGYPT

I am called Azza,
but that is not all . . .

My father says

أنت أبو الهول

(an'-tah ah'-boo el ho'-le)

"You are a sphinx."

My grandfather says

يا عين أُمك

(yah ein om'-mahk)

"You are the eye of your mother."

My mother says

ربنا يكثر من أُمثالك

(rab'-beh-na yeh'-ka-tar min am-tha-lek')

"May God multiply those who resemble you."

BUT THIS IS

THE REAL ME!

I live in ITALY

I am called Giuseppe,

but that is not all . . .

My mother calls me

"Cocchino di mamma"
(kok-kee'-noh dee mam'-ma)

"My darling little egg."

My father calls me

"Il mio caro angioletto"
(eel mee'-oh kah'-roh an-joh-let'-toh)

"My dear little angel."

My grandmother calls me

"Il mio pupetto"
(eel mee'-oh poo-pet'-toe)

"My very tiny one."

BUT THIS IS THE REAL ME!

I live in NIGERIA

I am called Adebayo,

but that is not all . . .

My father calls me
"Ehọnọ"
(ae'-oh-noh)

"Wild animal."

My mother calls me

"Chenchi"
(chin-chee)

"Bedbug."

My uncle says

"Ibu Agu"
(ee'-boo ah'-goo)

"You are a tiger."

BUT

THIS

IS THE REAL ME!

I live in CHINA

I am called King, but that is not all . . .

My mother says

心 肝
(syin-gan)

"You are my heart and liver."

My father says I am

小犬
(syau-chywan)

"A little dog."

My auntie calls me

小甜瓜
(syau-tyan'-gwa)

"Little sweet melon."

BUT THIS IS
THE
REAL

ME!